AN INTRODUCTION

......to cross the bridge of imagination,
finding wonder in the mundane
and splendour in the familiar.
And where we wander in the timeless mind,
alive entwined the past and future.
And like a river the present permanent runs
where we see that though each life unique
all lives are one......

The Iron Bridge
by
John Ward

Drawings by Mark Burrell

Published by FERINI DESIGNS - Interior Design - Gallery - Photographic Studio
Design and Layout John Ward and Michaela Barber

ISBN 0-9541912-2-6

27 -29 All Saints Road
Pakefield
Lowestoft
Suffolk
NR33 0JL
Tel:01502-562222
email: ferini.designs@virgin.net
web: www.ferinidesigns.co.uk

Printed by RICHARDSON PRINTING
44 Pinbush Road
South Lowestoft Ind Est
Lowestoft Suffolk
NR33 7NL Tel:01502-516991

Foreword

It was some years ago that I met John; it may have been at an opening, and of course, I had heard of him and his music. He had just released the CD 'Waking Dreams' a copy of which he gave to me. I was stunned by the visual words and music and it struck a chord deep within me. At some point I mentioned that if he ever wanted a cover painted I'd be happy to do it.

Moving on a couple of years he brought round the poem story 'The Iron Bridge'. Again I was deeply touched, seeing that it was brimming full of wonderful images. I said I would love to do some drawings and over the last few years have been doing just that. Of course these are only a few of the many drawings and paintings contained within the poem.

I have tried to capture the feeling of this poem in my work along with my feelings about the place in which I was born and live. As a child I spent much of my time in Whapload Road, living there twice; once when the village was full of people and then later when they were gone and only the ghosts were left, but a great time for us boys to go exploring all those empty sheds and cottages.

With regard to feeling versus topographical accuracy, I have aimed at the former trying to invoke the story in each picture, not just as a specific poem moment, but as the poem overall as well. It has been a privilege working with John who greatly and gently helped me. I hope I have done justice to his poem that somehow has so much of my own life in it, and I am sure many other people's too.

Just one thing. I do know that Vikings don't have horns on their helmets, but in my dream they do.

Mark Burrell

About Mark Burrell

Mark Burrell's work has been exhibited in Lowestoft and the surrounding area, and also widely across the UK. Notable venues that have shown paintings have been The Royal Academy, London, as well as at the Royal Over-Seas League where he won the Lucy Morrison memorial prize for oil painting as well as in New York, France, Norway and Holland.

Mark has been featured in several programmes for television, notably on Moving Art, hosted by George Melly, where he was awarded 1st prize by Bill Oddie and was interviewed by Sister Wendy Beckett.
More recently he won 1st prize locally for the architectural drawing of 'Windy Day' that was drawn for this book.

These richly drawn works come from a world that sometimes touches the edge of dreams, but never falls into mere fantasy. For if we look we find a tight thread of reality running through them, the people, places and physical ghosts who occupy his vision sometimes mirror and occupy our own life journey, our feelings, uncertainty and our hopes.

With thanks to the following individuals that helped me to make this project possible;

A thousand thanks to David Butcher and Ivan Bunn for their initial inspiration and who so successfully excited the imagination of younger ears.

To Mark Burrell whose work I have admired for many years and who has created such wonderful images from this text

To Xenia Horne who has helped with all the organisation of every aspect of the ongoing project.

Also to Michaela and Paul at Ferini Designs for all their hard work.

To Lynne for her time and support.

Across the iron bridge there lies
the spiral streets that twist and dive
the corner ways and alleys blind
where if eyes and ears are opened up
the scenes and shows don't slow nor stop,
amongst these stones and brickwork lines
amongst these carbon covered shops
amongst these scores and wrinkled lanes,
caught in countenance sublime
in fissured faces settled there
the age etched maps of life and time.
These rocks and soil, sea and sand
shape the face behind the hand
that shapes the land and builds a town
that traps and holds them hard and bound
to trudge the streets and wear them down,
but the ghosts of stone store the steps
of the dead that walk this way,
the clammy cobbles worn and grey
the wooden doors and walls engraved
with graffiti ground like epitaphs
proclaiming love and stating hate,
sharp new scars and fading dates
across the town the red brick waits
the latest hands to carve the cry,
the ancient words, the oldest lines
Jimmy
      loves Ruth
            forever.........

Youth clubs and pubs,
the sweat shop night spots,
crammed with the jabber of couples' conversation and the insistent monotone
bedroom beat of a drum box.
Locked in an embrace
Jimmy and Ruth's hearts race as they sway ungracefully across the flashing floor.
Nothing more is needed
as the first flames of young love ignite in their hearts, heads and loins,
consuming and then consummated
                later in the night.........

The orange lights gild the wet streets as they leave,
as the crowds on the corners tuck into takeaways and shout loudly across the road.
The boys in their best white shirts,
the girls with their arms crossed across their chests
doing their bare best to keep warm in their black slit short skirts and topple-high heels.
Jimmy's beery breath hangs in the air,
his jacket around Ruth's shoulders as she shudders in the one o' clock shadows,
heading for home, surrounding one another.
He sez he 'lovesa' and she smiles,
hiding her head in his chest
as they walk awkwardly in a cold caress to a south side bedsit block.
                              He stops.
                              Fumbles and unlocks.
                              She stumbles,
                                        blindly in.

The anonymous numbers on the dirty doors
the stale food smell on every floor,
the echoing steps on the carpet-less stairs
the unwanted papers,
the onion air.
                    Still, they scuttle and scuff and leave them there,
                    complete the climb
                    and close the door.

There, amongst the CD cases and coffee cups
on the floor,
watched by the posters
hung up
on the wall,
together,
on the sunken sofa,
they play the game.
                    The talking,
                    the tempting,
                    the teasing and touching,
                    the kissing and caressing.
                    They make love..........
                                        A baby cries in the room above
        and a fire truck passes
        its rousing siren racing to dowse the flames
        in some other part of town.
        Jimmy and Ruth cool down,
        their blaze burnt out,
        leaving their hearts to hope,
                        and the unspoken doubt

The milkman comes,
rattling and humming,
clanking and clinking,
like a glass glockenspiel, delivering down the empty avenues,
grinding his boots on the abrasive pavement
moving through the grey pallid air.
Nothing else seems alive save the early sparrows that chirp and chatter on the chimneys
and a crypt-black cat slinking back towards home.
The stone sleeps and the leaves weep with dew,
all is suspended
awaiting the sun and the first car,
even the litter in the gutter barely rustles
while the sea softly sighs
hung
between tides,
lying unseen behind the houses.
                              Then,
                              like a suddenly-struck bell,
                                        the sun bursts,

furnace forged and newly lit,
its blood orange rim rushing up
reviving and flushing the face of the sky,
spilling flame into the waves
and splaying colour across the east faced walls of the ashen town.
Each unique brick is outlined,
every mosaic shade defined,
the entire tapestry of masonry clarified
as the night is defied
once more.
The croaking guttural gulls glide and soar through the razor edge air,
clean and cold
white wings unfolding
while a slick starling sings,
clicking and stuttering
away on the wire.
A guttering car coughs into life,
revs and roars away,
the working
day has begun.

Outside the fish shop a lorry unloads its ice lain slippery silver.
The school leaver, ring-eared and eyed
stumbles, leaden-legged with each crate
onto the cold counter,
cursing under his visible breath
and slouching under the weight of the morning.
The wailing shipyard siren signals the end of another shift
and the red eyed, grey faced wrights drift from the gates wobbling
two-a-breast on black bikes escaping
to a restless bed
in a tip-toe home.

     Deano stands alone,
     taking his position
     outside the train station.
     Waiting and watching,
     grumbling into his grizzled broom beard,
     moist with his meths breath,
     taking another choking swig at the brown bagged bottle in
     his great coat pocket;
     passed by the increasing cars,
     by the cyclists
     heads down, legs peddling,
     noses running.

The unlocking shop keepers, yawning,
unfurl awnings,
sweep doorways and dress windows,
arrange displays with the day's news honed into headlines;
sandwich boarded
seductive, sordid
blaring affairs of the famous and the secrets of Sodom,
come in and buy 'em,
     you could win a million.
But,
late and flustered,
agitated and clustered
the cars go by 'em and become stagnated,
locked in lines as the iron bridge rises………

The river's the reason this town has arisen,
It's placed its position,
governed its growth
its style and condition.
It brings prosperity
and the dirtiest poverty.
It flows gently,
the curse of the car in this accelerated age......

Back in other modern times it needs no apology,
the vein and the artery that pours life from and to the town's heart.
Now, no more than a memory away it lies,
the landscape of youth alive in minds
that survive old age and even death
(where these head held pictures are given breath
and allowed to excite the imagination of younger ears).
Not sepia, nor black and white,
they call back the years
when the canvas of a thousand drifters cut the air;

Wings of ochre across the docks,
like giant moths
their incisive scimitar geometry flapping,
slapping as the wind is captured in cloth the colour of rust and mustard
marked and numbered
spread gull-high above the long low hulls of black and red,
green and blue,
their bows embellished with cherished names proclaiming that this is:
'The Star of Hope', 'The Sarah Hide'
'The Halcyon', 'The Pride'.
'The Constant Friend' and 'Consolation',
'The Reunited' and 'Resolution'.
'The Osprey' and 'Swift Wing'
'The Three Kings' and 'Quiet Waters'.
'The Orion', 'Defender'
'The Paradox' and 'Peace Maker'.
From dockside to dockside an incredible jungle of jostling masts, ropes and rigging
reach towards the late September sunshine
while the slender willie woodbine funnels
chug their smut black breath from red hot hidden hearts.
Up the quay crunching carts clatter and rattle
taking tackle, warps and ropes to the waiting boats.
Horses snort as hooves of iron scrape on stone
while the flesh and bone of barefoot boys
slip on the unforgiving ground.

All around the unrelenting race of the market place pushes on.
The harvest is full and the harbour heaves with two hundred drifters,
twisting, shifting, turning,
churning white water, burning furious coal
in the crush to get closer to the quay and a crab claw hold on that
precious landing place.
Gasping for space, beams bend, groan, creak and crack
as wood presses hard onto wood
and a rising flood of impatient shouts tumble
as tempers like capstans strain.
Pushing amongst the clotted crowd,
varicose face inflamed,
the harbour master is at pains to keep the place in order.
He bellows through his bristling beard and above the battling noise,
        "C'mon boys, let go that bloody rope!"
his authority met with frustrated ribald rebellion.
        "Bugger off!" someone offers
as the capstan is turned another notch and the crush increases.
        "Alright, I'll cut the flaming thing," he answers
and brings his axe down to hack the heaving hemp
relieving some pressure from the impossible bottleneck.
                        Still the cram continues though.
                        The gluttonous gulls bark and wheel,
                        below, the market deals and seethes,
                        its air crowded with cries,
                        and the dense sea smell of fresh fish and filthy smoke.
                        People choke when they breathe
                        as sail succumbs to steam.

From the Denes Eileen surveys the view with her gentle Highland eyes
while her hard hands reveal the herring's guts
as quick silver cuts silver.
Looking bulky in her apron and oily,
her fingers bound,
the blue wrap around her face frames fair skin reddened by the autumn chill
and a strand of dark hair dangles above eyes so deep
they recall the lochs of home.

An uprooted flower from the far isles,
she follows the fishing
guts its herring
watches its seasonal cycle re-enacted in each east coast port,
as it winds its way southerly.

Such a far cry from those Hebridean hills;
those still, hazy, rainy mountains,
the heathers' whispering blanket,
blown beneath the buzzard's circle and its high lonely mew.
A few whitewashed crofts nestled
smoking in the folds of the dark familiar land,
her Father's calloused hand holding hers as they join the set
circling at the hot, merry ceilidh,
and her Mother's woven stories
spoken magically in another tongue.
                                        Such a far, long cry
                                                for one so young.

But these home thoughts do not tarry long
as she stands here now chatting with Kathleen or singing songs,
both filleters when they were thirteen
a seemingly long
                    six
                        summers
                            ago....
They cut and gut as though on automatic at a cracking impossible pace
that slurs the eye to a blur and yet so precise they slice through three thousand
fish an hour.
Julie, beside them, collects and beds the herring in seams of salt,
entombed in tubs to travel the world
they ride on endless fiery rails to land-locked Birmingham or Manchester,
shipped by steam and sail to Russia and America
making meals for millions and money for some with their sterling gleam.
        "Did you hear about Jenny?" says Kathleen.
        "She found out her young man, whitsisname, Sam,
        she found out he'd been cheatin' on her."
        "No" says Julie astonished.
        "Aye, saw him in the queue at the Royalty wi' 'is arm through another lassie's."
        "No"
        "Aye, so you know what she did?" continues Kathleen with a chuckle
        "She cries out, what do you think you're doin' you wee beggar!
        And, wi' knittin' needles in hand, goes off after him."
        "Och, she always was a fiery one" says Eileen,
        "So she is, but that's no' all. The other lassies wi' 'er, there was Moll 'n'
        Dollina and a few others, take up the chase and they're away,
        past Union Place,
        past the shipyard, hard on his heels."
        "Did they catch the rascal?" Julie asks with a mixture of alarm and amusement,
        "No, thank the Lord, they didnae, though I dread to think what would ha'
        happened if they had o' done."
        "It's a good job he could run" says Eileen, "I reckon these wee herrin' ha' got
        more guts than him."
        They all giggle and grin but stop abruptly when Julie whispers hoarsely,
        "Look out here comes Kill!"

The boss,
his small ferrety face
sharp like the wicked East wind,
wrinkled like a piece of flotsam,
creases as he comes across with staccato steps.
"C'mon you lot,"
his voice rattling as it battles with the phlegm
in the back of his throat.
"You're not gettin' paid to laugh and play around,
let's have less of the chatter and more of your
minds on the job."
The girls, who hadn't actually stopped, put their heads down and speed up,
as 'Kill or Cure,' scuttles off,
throwing a backwards glance.

A safe silence passes before Kathleen asks,
"Are you off to the dance th'morrow night?"
"Aye, I hope so, but no' with that tight miser" says Eileen
nodding towards Kill's disappearing, swaggering back.
"He couldnae get one of these dead fish to go wi' 'im" laughs Julie.
"Anyway though, I expect you'll be hoping to see that Joe Catchpole unless I'm
very much mistaken."
Eileen blushes.
"Aye, she's quite taken wi' 'im" says Julie with a wink.
"I don't care what you think" Eileen replies
  lifting her head haughtily and closing her eyes,
"I don't care whether he's there or no' "
                                    she lies.

The chat continues as the sky dissolves through soaring blue
into deepening evening.
The naphtha lamps are lit and flare
their warm fumes filling the air
and wafting with the Highland songs
piping their sublime melancholy along the lines of working women.
Each face is traced and suffused,
every shadow enhanced by the carnelian glow,
while the night brings visions of the dance
and daring dreams of Joe.

Across the tramlines,
over the smoke licked slate roofs
through the gas glow roads
just a black backed gull's short soar away he sits
sealed behind the sanctuary doors of the Triangle Tavern.
The alcoholic heat-scented draught meets the incoming men
as does the leaping laughter and the billowing bubbly flood of unfettered chatter.
Sawdust scattered across the floor soaks the wasted ale
as the dark wooden walls suck in the scene.

A thick blue grey shag haze hangs wraith-like about the heads of the
glistening raucous fishermen
bedecked in their best swagger suits, leather boots and wrappers,
while a melancholic concertina plays a plaintive melody
dipping and swirling its reedy carousel of sound around their ears.
Jugs of beer go gushing into mugs and glasses,
slopping and soaking into oaken tables,
sliding down open throats,
savoured and praised in a reverie of release and a song of celebration for a spell on shore….
   Thirty-six hours before they return once more to the slavery sea,
   their backs lashed with salt whips,
   their hands ripped on rough ropes,
   sleeping where they stand,
   forty-eight hours without stopping before
   collapsing into bunks like coffins
   crammed like the herring they catch into one hatch,
   guzzling grub round one tiny table
   as they ride the wild waters mountains and valleys,
   watching the wind at a whim sculpt the sea from a sleeping beauty
   to a fist of fury.

Though death's face, shaped from the waste of waves, has roared at them,
open-mouthed,
eddy-eyed,
his vast net close
his fast hands heaving hard,
they have survived,
   this time
   and upon their return burn their painfully earned pennies
   in a rush of living.
   Life on land is not big enough to harm them.

Jagged, hacking voices by the bar break the atmosphere
and turns the room around as the sound of inebriated insults spit.
A shattering glass rings like a boxing bell to commence a bout,
Some one is hit
and amid shouts two bodies tussle and grapple,
white knuckles locked in a drunken ineffectual fight
lurching elephant-seal-like on the spot,
each trying not to let the other go.
Their friends move in to prise them apart,
and, once they have a hold, the two become more bold,
chests inflated outward
fingers stabbing,
jabbing accusations.
"Let me at the bastard" the bigger one bellows
as he's bundled to the door in a stumbling tangle of tripping feet and twisted arms.
"Let me loose" he growls
and as they do, he misses the step.
His blind boot treads air and he falls, flailing into the street

The smaller man thumps his mug on the bar with a snort,
"I could've 'ad 'im" he mumbles,
"No trouble, easy meat."
They all nod, to his face, as the pace settles again and the gabble resumes.

Just across the room sits Joe,
eyes alight with ale, playing dominoes with his mates.
"Is'at right you gotta date 'amorrow, Joe?" says one with a wink to another.
"Well, not an actual date, y'know, the usual thing,
I can take or leave her, makes no odds."
He shrugs and sups, shielding his face behind the mug.
"I reckon this one's a bit special though,
you not gonna go all soft on us now are you, you old sod?"
"What me? No,
just one of those Scots girls. Now c'mon,
who's got all the twos?"
"Thasright, but I know who, have you seen her?
I'd be in there right away if I had half a chance."
They all cackle and wise-crack.
Joe tries, but as he lays a double one
his mind's at the dance....

> The soft thud and scuffle of feet on floorboards
> brushing round the church hall at Union Place.
> The scraping chairs and chatter reverberating round
> the rafters, pinned with paper bunting.
> The one wall lined with fidgeting cross legged girls
> giggling, unkind, feigning to ignore the opposite lads,
> who, leaning or sat stick straight,
> wait with nervousness masked
> the moment to ask to take the floor.

A hoarse fiddle finds the tune
while a percussive piano plays the way for feet to follow
as they take up the tempo
and turn it to the first clammy touch of self-conscious courtship.
Quickstep couples swirl and dip,
the young girls watched by strict-mouthed sharp-eyed chaperones,
grown sisters and senior women
wary that no-one's left alone and no dance grows too close.
Joe gets nowhere near.
Fear has fattened his tongue
and his lead like legs are numb
unable to carry him across the crowded floor to Eileen.
Now the last waltz has come,
his final time to take the plunge
he is lunged into turmoil,
his mind embroiled in battle,
his heart enlarged rapidly pumps
                              and jumps
                                        and swamps his chest
though he does his best to calm the inner argument.

Flattening his hair with trembling hands,
flicking his velvet collar free from fluff,
he stands and scuffs across with faltering feet
the awful infinite miles to meet Eileen.
Prim and preened, she looks perfect
in her one and only best cotton dress,

> he takes a breath and says,
> "May I?" Voice dry,
> she answers "Yes,"
> averting her eyes.

He sighs
and as she rises to take his hand,
stands on her toe.
She yelps, he tries to help
as she rubs her offending foot and bites her lip.
He apologises,
rolls his eyes skywards as his friends snigger
and he feels a bigger fool than he did before.
They try once more,

> pausing, positioning,
> finally stepping as one,
> face to face,
> palm to palm,
> beneath the beams of Union Hall
> they dance to the tune of 'Endearing Young Charms.'

As the final note fades
and the last happy hand quietens,
the delighted dancers bustle through the double doors.
They course down the steep steps,
scrunch and click onto cobbles, chiming 'cheerios,'
dissolving into the early night and leaving the yellow light that falls from the
windows of the hot hall.
Stalling by the wrought iron railings, Eileen stands with Julie and Kathleen
waiting, as Joe walks over, cap in hand.

> "Can I walk you home" he says.
> "Aye, if you want" she replies,
> and suddenly home doesn't seem
> so very far away.

Wandering through the warm dusty roads
and across the open space of the town's sleeping market place,
the four talk softly as the night spreads upwards from the hollow black echoing alleys
into the dying summer sky;

> crystal marine green rises to infinite sapphire,
> the diamond fire of Venus flickering aloft,
> the flint face smoke houses venting their wood
> scented clouds across the slate and terracotta tiles.

A merry music hall crowd outside the Royalty
revel in a bawdy chorus as they clamber aboard a clattering tram,
trundle and sway around the corner,
giving way to the horse-drawn water wagon laying the day's dust.
A group of fisher girls strolling by say goodnight, knitting as they go,
as Eileen and Joe stroll through station square, where the steaming trains seldom cease,
and stop at the iron bridge.
"I'll be at sea for a spell from 'amorrow" he says,
"But as soon as I'm home would you like to see a play at the Hippodrome with me?"
"I don't know, maybe" she teases.
"I'd be very pleased if you would."
"Good" she says with a smile, "I'd like to."
Joe's oval face flushes, feeling a mile high.
"It's been a long hot summer" he sighs, not sure what next to say.
"Aye" she answers, "The best."
They stand and gaze out past the pier
its length alight with life,
a red beacon blazing at its end.
A friendly harvest moon rises
amber from the edge of the sea
busy with countless black boats
reflecting their lamps in leaping liquid silver shapes
as they tramp to and from the freight-filled quays and the perpetual market.

Far further out
        the east is stirring with a storm.
        White flashes like magnesium flares,
        rumbles like cannons on the distant air
        and where youth's rosy blush now blooms
        there is soon the rush of bloody poppies.

The iron bridge slowly closes
and the wall once more becomes a road.
Starting motors choke and rasp
making cumulus smoke spiral from trembling exhausts
and the long line of idling cars to throb as throttles take the pressure
of impatient feet.
        The opposing ends get set,
        eyes meet,
        and steadily the thin red line of rattling barriers swing
        skyward.
        The race resumes.
Face to face
across the bridge
amidst the fumes
the uptight drivers stab their feet down
and rush toward each other, joust-like.
Tottering bikes
jostling pedestrians,
the iron bridge rumbling and clanging like a giant tin drum, vibrating
as it takes the weight of a town in motion;

pushing forwards,
rushing past the rusting anchors
past the arcades blinking bandits
through the crossing's flashing amber
by the gift shop's tourist trinkets
by the billboard's bright temptation
past the patchwork grey stained station,
passing Deano stood unsteady,
past the pubs and Chinese chippie
by the glass house office storey
round the islands green oasis
the one way, two lane stampede races,
by the regimented terraced faces
each row reading by its spaces
like a book, spells out the places
of the bomb sites in the war.......

Huddled on the floor,
beneath the table,
clutching cushions
Mary cuddles her kids as fire falls from the sky.
The crumpled air thumps and tears and thuds shudder
through the trembling ground.
Hearts pound,
the youngest child cries despite the soothing sounds
that whisper from Mary's lips.
She strokes the toddler's hair,
"Ssh there"
she sighs.

Suddenly, somewhere close by
a short glissando whistle cuts and erupts in the sick compressed crunch of destruction.
Convulsions crease the agonised air, writhing mutated
while the earth alive lurches like a retching drunkard,
contorted in the chaos that make the safe foundations shake
and the dark room reel.
The ceiling sheds some slow motion plaster dust,
the doused lampshade swings
and as Mary clings to her children, a china child topples from the mantle piece
and shatters on the tiled hearth.
The receding roar sends rustling soot scuttling down the chimney,
settling gently on the white fractured fragments of the forlorn ornament.
"Christ, that was close" George, the eldest child says.
"You watch your language" Mary chides,
"I'm gonna look"
"You come away,"
he disobeys, rises and parts the thick curtains
that suck up the dangerous light.

Through the taped windows the night trembles and the town cowers,
its chimneys silhouetted against a sky enraged with the bloody glow of
burning homes.

The shooting star arc of white tracer hones in on the unseen attackers
as ack-ack splinters and explodes
and across the road two moving figures are frozen in the flash,
fleetingly,
then are gone like ghosts.
The sweep of the searchlight's swords slice through the smoking darkness
trying in vain to pinpoint the psychopathic planes
eventually paling against the menacing bombers' moon hung high above it all
like a friend to the foe.

> "You get under here at once, or you'll get a thick ear"
> hisses Mary, glaring to conceal her fear with her
> angry stare.
> George, more scared of his mum's hand than where
> the bombs are landing,
> bends beneath the table and sits at arm's length
> awaiting the inevitable tongue lashing, when, the
> destruction stops;

> > A ticking clock,
> > a pensive breath,
> > a sniffling child.
> They force their ears but hear just one more distant
> rapid crack of gunfire
> then the welcome winding wail of the all-clear siren
> swooping down the stressed streets,
> settling
> like warm spring sunlight on the hunched shoulders
> of each below bed, under stair, table tucked
> sweat scared soul in hiding.

The siren fades to fire truck bells,
footsteps running, yells,
the smell of Hell's heat scorching through the torched town,
the pound of wounded walls crashing down, smashing
seething slates and boiling bricks.
Tongues of fire lick along the line of bombers' welts
from Love Road to Summer Lane dealt with the nameless flaming hand
of random death.
From the Hippodrome through London Road's terraced homes,
across to the cliff top thatch church of St. Peter's scattering incendiary sparks
into the stellar night
figures fight with fraught phantom features
sometimes outlined in the hot light, grim and sweating,
then silhouetted like shadow puppets, hauling buckets hand to hand
or standing peddling at pumps and manhandling the heavy hoses.
Each fire like a flare throws a guiding light
on which the sightless bombers can hone
and whose next wave may drone out of the ominous east at any moment.

On the edge of the ocean like a beacon
the broken church burns and beckons
and each fireman, aware of the precious seconds,
dashes to dampen the lantern that threatens to open the night
to further destruction.
                        Alive with fire the grave-stones flicker
                        black and bright,
                        crooked and upright,
                                            like twisted untamed teeth,
                        like Hades' hungry jaws have yawned open
                        to devour the church, tower and all,
                        from the fury below.
                        The rafters' perishing embers glow,
                        the ribs of the roof revealed
                        as the thatch skin is peeled in the funeral pyre
                        of a thousand prayers
                        murmured on cracked lips,
                        mixed with curses cried in angry despair
                        as the give-away glare leaps and eats voraciously
                        through the thin security of night's cape.
                        Lookouts wait,
                        pushing their ears,
                        throwing their sight,
                        wrenching their senses to anticipate the hatred
                        that might come droning over the eastern
                        horizon at any time.
                                        Instead,
                                            silent and fine,
                        a more welcome vision takes shape in the
                        squinting distance.
                        "Look!" someone cries, "A mist."
                        And, like a miracle,
                        like a visible wish made material by the strength
                        of a thousand thoughts thrown desperately as
                        one at the mirror moon,
                        a fog is forming.
                        First phantom faint, looming,
                        a pale line, creeping ill-defined from the darkness,
                        then, slowly swallowing the sea,
                        smothering the stars,
                        dissolving the moon, crawling,
                        a white wall fingering the shore,
                        setting a ceiling on the sky
                        and blinding the bombers' crucifix sights.

Now the town is slowly covered,
the sharp flames smudged, water-washed and squashed,
their colours compressed and the thick smoke smothered
as the fog's fingers myopically grope
corpse white and cloister cold down the shadowy alleys.
It lingers on the corner like a whore and
like a thief, creeps round the doors
flirting with the secret keyholes.
It feels the steps
fills the hollows
strokes the cobbles and deadens the din,
making shadow plays and wraiths of the fireman
that rush out and in of the pulsing orange glow.
It grows,
spreading its slight of hand through the threaded streets
and the web of tangled terraces,
absorbing the night till dawn's anaemic light
comes seeping down and casts its weary sight on the reeking rubble and ruin.
Ink smudge starlings sit silent on the chimneys,
the slanting soot grey slates,
the taped windows,
the drawbridge garden gates and the street met steps
that separate in one stride the pavement from the home inside.

Beyond the front door,
set to the back of ninety seven Seago Street,
in the scullery, Mary quickly brews the breakfast tea.
Damp washing hangs lank from a line strung sloping across the ceiling.
George sits beneath at a small wooden table
inspecting his bread and dripping,
                humming,
                legs swinging,
                with baby Lizzie beside him
                busy on the sleeve she's sucking,
                dropping her food on the cold lino below.
Mary cuts the bread, lights the stove,
Lizzie grizzles…..
           The asthmatic kettle whistles
           and with a tea towel wrapped around the handle
           Mary drowns the dark dust
           in the bottom of the cracked floral pot.
           There's a knock at the door
           and with a shoulder shove and a rickety rattle Mary's
           sister stumbles into the steaming scullery.

"Aunty Dotty!" shouts George

"It's a bit sticky" says Dotty wiping her feet.

"Bloomin' thing's swollen with the damp" says Mary,

"Pull up a pew"

"Ta"

"Aah, I'm so tired" sighs Dotty as she tousles George's hair

and tickles Lizzie,

"Seems like the whole town was alight last night."

"I know" says Mary, "if it hadn't been for that fog.....

well, it was the hand of God."

"The hand of Hell more like" snorts Dotty

"I saw only the hand of hell last night."

"Oh I was so frightened" says Mary,

"I kept thinking of you, driving out there,

scares the life out of me, was there any casualties?"

"I did thirteen runs, there was some dead among 'em"

answers Dotty quietly.

"I do wish someone else would drive that ambulance" says Mary.

But there's only silence from Dotty

as she sips her watery tea.

The toast tans and the frying pan spits

as an egg hits the blue fume fat.

"Have you heard from Peter yet?"

asks Dotty after a while.

"Not a word. The last letter I did get was silly it was so censored.

I wrote but he never answered......it's been so long."

"I don't expect there's anything wrong" Dotty reassures,

"The post is so slow at the moment."

"Oh I know" sighs Mary, "But I'm very worried,

I don't know where he is or even if he's......"

The air swallows her sentence

as she becomes re-aware of

George's fidgety presence.

She glances to Peter's black and white sightless eyes

that stare down from a shelf upon the son they reflect

and at the daughter they've yet to see.

"Patience" says Mary, more to herself, "He'll be fine,

time will send us news of his good health.

It'll be a better letter for the wait I reckon 'a George?" she winks.

"Hey, I'd better go!" exclaims Dotty suddenly,

checking the clock and slurping her drink,

"I've got to be back at the factory in half an hour.

I hate that place, it's so noisy, and it stinks."

She kisses Lizzie who's shouting to get out of her chair

and pretends to punch George on the jaw as she heads for the difficult door.

"Hang on!" cries Mary

"How's that fella of yours? Have you seen him recently?"

"Oh, only a couple of days ago,
we went to see 'Pimpernel Smith' at the Hippodrome,"
"Oh that old flea pit."
"Not any more, it was hit last night,
although they say it might be alright.
I don't think it was ever so bad."
"At least with a hole in the roof there'll be more light
to keep an eye on Jack the Lad's wandering hands" says Mary saucily.
"You know what those sailors are like when they're back on land."
"I'll make the most of him while I can" Dotty replies,
flashing a grin and rolling her eyes.
                                        She steps outside.
"It's beginning to brighten, I'd say" she calls,
"Cor c'n I go 'n' play then" shouts George.
"Alright, go on" says Mary, "but mind you don't get dirty!"
But he's gone,
with a backward wave and a
"Bye bye Aunty Dotty," he runs out the back
and through the narrow side alley to the street,
passing the postman on the pavement as he goes.
"Hello there" he says,
                        but there's no reply from the postman today.

George and the boys are belting down the back alleys,

                                    bouncing wall to wall
                                    rough 'n' tumbling
                                    shoe scuffing football,
                                    falling on to scabby knees,
                                    hitching sliding socks
                                    smearing snotty sleeves
                                    with back hand handkerchiefs.

Mean soles slap back reverberation ringing from the high brick boundaries
of cramped back yards,
huddled beneath flags of sodden washing
strung between land lubbered, garden planted drifter masts.
Tripping into the maze of roads
they dash along the terraced roads and razed homes that sit like gaps of extracted
teeth in the street's jaw.
The war has stalled the car's onslaught for now and the released streets are the
backdrop and landscape for a million youthful capers and childhood games.
                Hide 'n' seekers
                cowboys 'n' Indians
                robbers 'n' cops
                heroes 'n' villains.
                Cricket with wickets chalked on the wall,
                football with goal post coats
                thrown with precision onto the ground.
                Spinning tops and roller skating,
                go carts and kiss chasing.

Skipping ropes and hopscotching,
playing dead and 'Beatcha' racing.
Shrapnel searching,
the boys go running towards St. John's Church,
spire encased to disguise its landmark target from hostile eyes.
Down along the edge of the prom,
past the thorn thick barbed wire beach, mined and alarmed
banned and barred to the simple stroll,
the soft sand sprouting angry metal
washed with a cavalry of brown winter waves
that are crowned with long white beards.
Over the iron bridge,
where the solemn grey military boats sway
berthed beside the converted mine sweeper drifters,
through station square
tearing past the Woodbine Café
on and up into the labyrinth of adventure.
The litter of last night's terror lies scattered throughout these entwined back streets
and the boys now slow to seek out what delightful debris they can claim.
It starts to gently rain and they stop to stare at where a bomb has found its mark.

The fine dark drizzle falls lazily,
compressing the hazy grey warm wood smoke smouldering,
seeping from the heat blackened beams of a burst house,
a home,
blown to bits.
Broken bricks, staggered
like
steps
climbing
to emptiness,
rising from the scattered slag of crushed slates
and the sad litter of familiar family life.
The remains of the wrecked roof sags,
seemingly melted,
torn and mutated,
serrated and charred.

Planks, splinters and shards, stick out at hard angles,
a tangle of rubble and rafters,
dagger glass,
crumbling plaster.
A mangled mess of a million fragments
Criss-crossed and collapsing inwards,
stabbing outwards at the accused sky that watches
shroud white and washed out.

A skeleton home,
bone broken and gutted,
a curtain, tattered
hanging limp like a defeated flag.

Floral wallpaper still stuck fast,
a photograph,
            fallen
                    frame fractured glass
                    scoring across the smiling family faces,
                    eyes time suspended,
                    looking forward forever.

Nearby, a white wet hand,
dirty and still,
fingers curled,
reaches out from the fallen walls.
Weary arms heave and haul the heavy debris,
                            steadily exhuming the bomb blast tomb
                            hewn into the terrace row of Love Road.
                            The shared load is lifted along a forlorn line of faces,
                            fatigued, foreheads damp and stuck with lank rain hair.
Wordless mouths and charcoal cheeks,
throats that can only utter the constricted sounds of limbs
aching in the oppressive atmosphere.
                            "C'mon lads, there's nothing for you here"
                            a gently stern voice says.
                            "Run along."
The boys scurry away hurriedly
looking for another place to play around on.

Up through Union Place they scamper,
past the makeshift café that's grown in the hall
pouring out strong tea and gentle sympathy,
rattling with a stick the stumps of the railings,
the iron harvested recently and melted in the furnaces of weaponry,
and the sorrowful flames of victory;
past the smoke houses,
through the market place
past the wooden shed shanty town allotments,
the wigwam bean poles and the old herring barrel water butts,
along by the bulk of the canning factory with its brick chequered chimney,
down to the little stream tributary that flows serenely,
                            almost invisibly through the town,
                            finally to be lost as food for the harbour.

They scatter the ducks with a stone and scarper
down to the tousled banks
where an Armada is made from sticks and string
racing in excited competition on the indolent ebb,
shouting to win,
encouraging the current to catch *their* vessel
only to groan as it slows in the reeds or stalls on the slovenly mud.

Here amongst the jungle weeds,
the sublime slime,
larks unfold
and a world of wonder unwinds.
All the treasure the river holds;
minnows, toads
sticklebacks and tadpoles,
little eels and water voles.
Daphnia dancing,
boatmen speeding,
secret slow worms,
overturned stones revealing
nervous newts and plump slugs squirming.
Rattling reeds that cover the moorhens headlong dash,
the piping coot,
the brash conspiring cuckoo calling to be wished upon.
Summer, scrumping fruits, sweeter for their danger,
willow fronds fondling the muddy water, giving a whisper
to the mute breeze, humming bumble bees
on the purple bristling thistles,
the spiteful stinging nettles
muddled amid the cool 'n' soothing doc leaves.

                                             And the river breathes...

it sighs the stories of generations,
moves the sails of imagination
as racing sticks become Viking ships
blown by the winds of legend that move
semi-concealed in the collective treasury of tongues,
spoken and sung
passing along and among the lines of lives and time
of when the river is wider.

Riding the full flood tide,
skirting the dark marshes of the risen river
wide with the pull of the moon,
pushed by the eastern breeze across the whale way, the iron ocean,
the low boats glide
laden with the might of Thor and the warring magical passion of Odin.

Orion rising crowns the Saxon soil.
The long curve of the lazy hill, still,
broken by the sloping silhouettes of the small wooden village.
The languid smoke wafts from the wattle and daub
and, coming big behind the ash and oak,
the orange orb of the murdering moon, rising.

Slipping silently on, save the slop and slap of the black waves on the clinker hulls,
the long ships drift.
The sleek arc lines
the scroll and serpent prows
the circle shields along the sides,
passing now the brooding bulk of the ancient bronze barrows,
semi-sentient,
dark and dormant,
embracing their long anonymous dead.
Only the plaintive pipe of a curlew,
the snipe's frightened flight,
the splash of a moorhen and the cry of a coot alert the night to the alien presence that
stalks the peaceful water.

On the slow hill the horses snort, their nostrils flare,
sensing something strange in the scent of the whispering wind,
while inside, the families, unaware, share their stories round the snapping fire.
The talking tongues of flame form and frame the scenes
as the children lean in and gaze
in a swirling haze of fantasy and ancestry,
slipping into sleep,
riding the tales in their dreams and on into bed.

Near now pulls the invisible dread,
closer to the shore, long oars at ease
edged only by the breath of the breeze, made manifest by movement
as it is caught in the taut sail.
Beneath it sit fifty faces,
pale with fear or flushed with the fervour of imminent attack.
Hands on hilts of swords of steel,
threading their forearms through the heavy shields
and murmuring protective prayers behind their briny beards.

The horses whinny, champ and kick,
the dogs are yelping and quickly the settlement men grab their spears and step outside
peering into the camouflage of darkness.
They hear nothing….
They narrow their eyes,
stand bolt straight,
then realise the dogs are silent.
Too late!
The savage weight of Scandinavian steel falls swiftly upon them.
Swords and screams cut the air,
thatch ignites spiralling orange sparks to join the scattered stars.
The mothers take flight,
stumbling from the sounds of slaughter
pulling their precious daughters and sons to the hill's brink and beyond,
scrambling through the tangled thicket,
crawling under cover beneath the barbed bramble and thick hazel boughs

panting and pounding now
like frightened foxes
they watch the village as it burns and bleeds below.
The soil soaks the blood,
then gives it up as it seeps into the cold
and innocent river.
It clouds the water for a moment then is carried away;
spiralling in the eddies,
dispersing into the river's memory,
and carried on towards the omnipotent ocean.

Through the spreading body of the embryonic settlement it flows,
shrinking as the village grows,
taking the waste from the latest invaders
as they, in turn, draw the life from its generous course.
It weaves its way amongst the wooden walls
that, superimposed the scavenged stone replaces.
The new born church grown at its centre,
the flint and plaster and frames of timber
rising and encroaching closer.
The filthy alleys cluttered by bakers, cobblers, grocers
engorged with the thick stink of spattered sewage and scattered scraps.

The main mud street and market place
packed with traders' cries,
geese, goats and squealing swine,
oak carts and yoked horses, snorting,
working folk about their bustling business,
bartering, buying then
dying by the score
as the sign appears on infected doors,
the handful of herbs that don't deter
the flea-borne plague that without mercy
tirades through these dirty streets,
draining them, shivering barren and bleak,
leaving the loved ones to weep as they reach
at the death cart that slithers and slowly creaks,
piled with a pyramid of the purple staring dead.

And on and ahead the river runs,
peacefully past the church of St. Peter's
filling the font with the baptism blessing
a witness to weddings that laugh by the doors,
supplying the very source of salvation
as the great fire rages
through kindling timber and parched tinder thatch,
voracious, spreading contagious
sparks that catch the close huddled homes,
the grimace and groan of heavy hands pulling
pail upon pail from the merciful stream.

The accusing current green with the weed that now hangs from her hair
as she is plunged panicking, chained to a chair,
choking and gagging, sobbing
submerged in ignorance and purged
in the malice of the Witch Finder General
who's terrible steps fill these superstitious streets
with a plague of paranoia and easy fear.
She catches his gaze,
he sizes her soul with his misogynist eye,
then hangs her for rumour, wives' tales
and a mole on her thigh.

Astride his steed, standing by the smokehouse wall
Cromwell, warts and all, patiently waits for the blockade to surrender.
His tired troops, soothed and cooled by the gentle river,
smoke, grumble and wonder when the wait will be over.
The cannon answers,
its smoking explosion scattering the royalists like pigeons and gulls,
as the river now pulls towards the arc of the bay,
the long bow beach bending away
nurturing gently the germ of industry in its sheltered palm.

The beached boats and barrels sprinkled about the busy shore
and, out in the calm,
black beyond the breakers,
the wooden luggers, moored at ease
disgorge their eclectic cargo;
salt and timber,
stone and paper
and, of course, the herring that grows to build the grasping harbour
arms embracing the full rigged clippers,
drawing tall ships towards the town's heaving bosom,
grown now with towering churches and chiming taverns
and through which the trembling river, now sunken,
passes by the Highland women
singing and gutting the silver darlings,
flows through boys playing Pooh sticks and Vikings,
out and into the iron bridge harbour
with a babble of voices and liquid laughter,
dispersing like light from a secretive prism
to the collective sense,
                         the ocean's wisdom.

The Siamese lovers, joined at the hip,
time on their hands and love on their lips
come crossing by the iron bridge with the
barriers risen
and slip down the sunlit side of London Road.

The metallic morning glows around them,
golden from the soft stone,
bright as bells, wide and welcoming,
framing Jimmy and Ruth as they chatter and giggle,
blind but to themselves,
meeting in the middle,
speaking a new language,
the ancient courting tongue coherent to young love alone.
Passing by the Hippodrome
with its billboards boasting the town's best bingo, Jimmy says,
"Do you fancy a go, y'know, later on?"
"What me? Don't be daft!"
"I thought it might be a laugh" says Jimmy with a grin.
"I don't know, maybe, we'll see."
She giggles again as they wend their way round the corner
and past the Woodbine Café where Dotty and Mary are just jostling their pram and push-chair beside the
door and stepping inside.

The fatty food, the smell of the fries
bacon butties and steaming tea rise to meet them with
a welcoming warmth.

The underhand men in their overalls staring,
laughing, cracking dubious jokes with their mouths full agape like their ogling eyes.
Just across from the docks, they sit and pick hands,
act hard as rocks,
with fags dangling between ingrained fingers,
lingering as long as they possibly can over a cup of tea and a fried egg sarnie.
Dotty and Mary,
a milky mug of coffee
drink and rock babies,
discussing their 'old men.'
"Out of work and under my feet" Dotty complains.
Mary's is absent,
"The kids can be a strain" she quietly says.
They talk about school days and noisy neighbours that sneeze through the tissue thin walls
and all of the fantasy changes they would make with just a little lottery or bingo break.
"I'd take us all off to the Caribbean" says Mary.
"America for me" states Dotty emphatically,
"Or anywhere, I don't care so long as I'm out of that stinkin' factory."
"A place with a pool,"
"No more late night lines,"
"Just buy myself some time" says Mary,
but her reverie is broken by the grimy men leaving,
wolf-whistling and wheezing,

laughing their way out of the ringing door.
Dotty rolls her eyes,
"Men," she tuts, "Brains in their flies."
They gather the cups as the clock calls time,
frowning as they pay up,
and step outside to the bustling street.

> Chatting as they go, they pass Joe,
> hands in pockets, staring at the posters
> in the Army Recruitment Office window,
> his hand on the door,
> making a move to stride inside.

The women walk by,
crossing at the corner to 'pop in the shops,'
pushing their children wide around Deano,
stood outside the station uttering obscenities and
"Spare some change for a cup of tea?"
set to the spot like the statue opposite in Station Square.

The warm air is turning hot
and an exodus is underway,
thronging to be quenched in the soothing sea.
Jimmy and Ruth wait for the cars at St. John's Court,
then quickly cross,
trotting by Dotty and Mary,
passing invisibly,
making their way with arm tucked towels down to the crowded prom.

They near the pier and the scent of sun oil
oozes up from the beach to meet them;
the sound of the applauding waves,
the laughter, screams and yells
the smells of Summer wrapped in paper,
fish and chips and vinegar vapour.
The chant of the bingo caller,
the mannequin man and the automatic parrot
chattering and squawking at the people walking by.
The prim prom's cracked tarmac vanishing beneath the shimmering liquid
lakes of heat that hover in the hollows,
scorching the soft feet of the children, smeared with ice cream moustaches,
dodging wasps,
stubbing toes,
running round without their clothes
feasting on succulent infinite rock, grit sprinkled sandwiches and flask tepid tea;
scampering down to the cobalt sea that's hung with a haze
and dotted with white yachts, the odd small fishing boat
and red 'n' yellow inflatable floats bobbing in the shallows.
The weary waves stroke the shore and surrender gently on the weed green groynes,
making a feint play to abduct the bright beach balls

falling far short of the pin-stripe deck chairs and the cluttered wall of wind breakers
that sprawl their patchwork quilt of carefree colour.
The thirsty mustard sand sucks the energy from the day
as beached bodies lay, languishing in lines under the blue hot sky
like sausages sizzling in grease beneath the grill,
their perspiring salt skin peeling,
yielding under the uncompromising heat.
Jimmy and Ruth dip their feet, shouting,
pulling their bellies in as they wade,
jumping the waves until they are brave enough to immerse themselves in
the biting brine.

> And George is not far behind,
> with the boys he comes running by and drops lengths of
> twisted twine hopefully over the harbour wall,
> catching crabs then playing football against the goal
> chalked pier,
> melting the lazy hours into one
> until the sun's power ebbs and the afternoon runs its course.

Disappearing, the balmy day is dowsed in a sibilant summer shower
and a sunset begins to crown the tired town.
The black chimneys, choked with archaic soot, silhouette shape the stained glass skyline.
Slate shoulders, thunder dark, slope down
reflecting mercurial in the low inconsistent sun
that dazzles occasionally from the cover of a cavernous cloud.

Rainbow rivulets run in the mucky gutters;
tangerine, turquoise, aquamarine and quartz
all caught in the prisms that pour into the grids of darkness
anointing the drains with the sun set's splendour.
Sinking, the fish-scale sky slips serenely as the night moves west,
growing as the gradient of colours turn gradually through
every blue into deepening darkness.
The shower sends Jimmy and Ruth running,
up through the sparse market place,
where the vegetable vendors and trinket traders are calling it a day,
and in through the doors of the Triangle Tavern.

> The alcoholic heat-scented draught meets them
> as does the leaping laughter
> and the billowing bubbly flood of unfetted chatter.
> Joe is in the corner mardling with his mates,
> Ruth sits down and waits for Jimmy to buy the beer.
> She feels a little uncomfortable here,
> her dark eyes catching no-one's as she glances round the rowdy room.
> > Young and working away from home;
> > a flower, pulled free from the season-less city
> > with its faded factories and vivid vacuity
> > visible in the numb eyes and screaming graffiti;

the growling blanket of turgid traffic
jammed beneath the pigeon's swooping flight
and drowning out its musical coo.
The choked view through the forest of flats
camouflaged by their monotony
where the steady hand of her anxious Mum
tends to her ailing Grandmother,
who, in turn, spends her days recounting her remarkable past
and sometimes an exotic story
told in her native tongue.

Ruth is quietly wondering how they both are,
head down,
winding a strand of black hair around her slender finger,
when Jimmy reappears, weaving from the crowded bar,
gripping tightly a pint and a half.
"You alright?" he asks, aware of the far-away look in her eyes.
"Fine, now you're back." She smiles and squeezes his hand.
They sit, relax and watch the one-man band,
singing almost to himself in the corner,
and dissect the day's events.
Laughing at the time spent burying each other in the sensual sand,
imagining plans drawn upon tomorrow's promise
and toasting their time together with another beer.

Suddenly, jagged hacking voices by the bar break the atmosphere
and turns the room around as the sound of inebriated insults spit.
"Time to leave I reckon" says Jimmy and,
in what seems like a split second, he finishes his pint
and guides Ruth to the door.
"I didn't want to hang around anymore" he says outside,
"Besides it's getting on for closing time.
Do you want to come back round mine?"
"You didn't have to ask" she replies. "C'mon"
and they set off,
Ruth leading the way;

past murmuring alleys where their steps bounce back,
along Love Road with the shapes in the shadows,
making them feel they are being followed,
letting them know they are not alone
and causing their shuddering backs to ache
with the gaze of invisible eyes.
They squeeze each other's hands tightly
and laugh undisguised at their silly stupidity
as they walk quickly by Union Place Hall,
just as a flushed dance crowd is turning out
and coursing merrily down beside the smokehouse wall.
Kathleen and Julie laugh and shout 'Goodnight!'
to the smiling Joe and Eileen

who brush past Jimmy and Ruth, unnoticed,
or, perhaps, unseen.
Down through Seago Street,
black as pitch,
where a dog barks and a curtain twitches,
a curious witness to their ephemeral footsteps,
suddenly lit by a flash of fleeting sheet lightning;
past the oasis of weedy allotments
past the empty, echoing station,
along by the locked gates of the silenced shipyard,
down to the bright and sleepless docks,
where the coloured lights merge in the motion of the harbour's murky black water
and a handful of sleeping trawlers are rocking in time to the gentle swell,
their anchor eyes weeping orange rust,
their beams folded like giant bats' wings;

by the busy freight quay
with it's crossed cranes slowly swinging,
stacking timber from Scandinavia and ore from South America,
and, beyond the halogen glare, the glowering mass of the grey grain silo
and the canning factory's dark stack gently fuming.
They continue walking, into the shadow of the frozen food works
where Ruth wearily toils from Monday to Friday;

past the fading fish market disgorging its sole,
cod, haddock and plaice
and, filling the space, on the edge of the sea,
the skeletal form of the unfinished gas rig
rising like a tower block above the docks,
adorned like a birthday cake with shimmering lights
and the violet spark of the arc welder's work.
High above, in the soft summer sky,
dry lightning flickers silently, reaching out from the east.
Orion rises,
and the ancient eye of the new moon watches Jimmy and Ruth
as they move slowly through the dreaming town
and over the iron bridge.

In the distance, the black block of St Peters church tower
winks a single white bulb atop its bare flag pole
and beyond, just visible
the long lazy line of Bloodmoor Hill twinkles with the lights
of the latest estate,
one warm point of which belongs to Mary,
as she sits, softly telling the children an ancient story,
watching them ride the tale into dreams and slowly slip
into sleep's magical voyage.
Jimmy and Ruth stroll on,
past the sentinel war memorial
with its scrolling roll call of names.
The anonymous fame of;

               Adams
               Butcher
               Bell
               Catchpole…..
The glorious fallen all
fishermen and ploughmen,
                      turned into gunners.
But Jimmy and Ruth don't linger to wonder at the
whispering epitaphs,
instead they stop at the brick bus stop to kiss,
and then with a silver coin he cuts,
grinding into the living brick and mortar
a proclamation for all time,
the ancient words, the oldest lines,
                  Jimmy loves Ruth forever……